PANDAS

Written and edited by **Barbara Taylor Cork**

Consultant Miranda Stevenson BA PhD
Curator of Animals, Royal Zoological Society of Scotland

TWO-CAN

First published in Great Britain in 1989 by
Two-Can Publishing Ltd
27 Cowper Street
London EC2A 4AP

3rd Impression 1991

© Two-Can Publishing Ltd., 1989

Text by Barbara Taylor Cork
Design by David Bennett
Printed in Hong Kong

British Library Cataloguing in Publication Data

Pandas.
I. Pandas — For children
599.74'443

ISBN 1-85434-090-5

Photograph Credits:
p.4 Bruce Coleman/WWF/Kojo Tanaka p.5 Zefa p.6 Bruce Coleman/WWF/Tim Rautert p.7 Bruce Coleman/WWF/Kojo Tanaka p.8 Ardea/Kenneth W. Fink
p.9 Ardea/Zoological Society of London p.10/11 Henry Ausloos p.12 (top) Zoological Society of London (bottom) Zoological Society of London/John Knight
p.13 Zoological Society of London p.14 NHPA/Philippa Scott p.16 WWF/K. Schaller WWF/Tim Rautert p.17 Jacana/D. Fiore Bruce Coleman/WWF Kojo Tanaka
Cover photo: Henry Ausloos

Illustration Credits:
p.1 Malcolm Livingstone p.3 Malcolm Livingstone/Alan Rogers p.4 Malcolm Livingstone p.9 Malcolm Livingstone p.11 Malcolm Livingstone
p.13 Malcolm Livingstone p.15 Malcolm Livingstone p.18-19 Alastair Graham p.20-24 Julie Park p.25 Alan Rogers p.27 Claire Legemah p.28-29 Malcolm
Livingstone p.30 Tony Wells p.31 Alan Rogers p.32 Malcolm Livingstone

CONTENTS

LOOKING AT GIANT PANDAS

Giant pandas are shy, gentle animals that live in the mountain forests of south-west China. They are one of the rarest animals in the world.

The Chinese people call giant pandas 'white bears' or 'large bear-cats' because they look like bears. Most scientists think that giant pandas are related to bears. But because giant pandas are very different from other bears, scientists put them in a separate family of their own.

Giant pandas have a strange pattern on their fur. They look as if they are wearing four long, black socks and have black goggles over their eyes. Their round ears are all black too. Male and female pandas look the same but the males are often a bit bigger than the females.

▲ Giant pandas have sharp hearing and a good sense of smell but their eyesight is not very good.

► In the mountains where giant pandas live, it often snows. Giant pandas love to play in the snow.

PANDA FACTS

Pandas love playing, especially when they are young. A panda can turn somersaults and stand on its head.

The giant panda isn't the only panda in the world. There is also the lesser, or red, panda, which is probably related to the raccoon family.

THE PANDA'S HOME

The mountains where the giant pandas live are often cloudy and misty and there are many deep valleys, waterfalls and streams. It is very cold and, in winter, there's lots of snow. The panda's thick, waterproof fur helps to keep it warm and dry. A panda even has fur under its feet.

The pandas live in forests of bamboo with some trees such as birch, maple, fir and spruce. They move about through tunnels in the bamboo. The pandas are so well hidden in these tunnels that it's hard to study how they live. There is still a lot we don't understand about how pandas live in the wild.

Pandas don't live in families. Each panda lives on its own in a small area of bamboo forest. This area is called its territory. A panda leaves scent at certain places in its territory. These scent marks usually tell other pandas, "I live here, keep out."

To escape from enemies, such as leopards or brown bears, a panda usually climbs a tree. The panda's black and white fur makes it hard to see against the black tree trunk and white sky. So a panda's markings may help it to escape from enemies.

But we don't really know why a panda has a black and white pattern on its fur. Some scientists think the colours are a warning to tell enemies to "Keep Away". A panda has strong jaws and sharp claws and will fight fiercely if it has to.

Pandas sometimes scratch trees and leave deep claw marks. They may do this to sharpen and clean their claws.

► Pandas are good at climbing trees, although they usually climb slowly. Their strong, curved claws help them to get a good grip on the tree trunk.

◄ In its mountain home, the panda moves quietly through the clumps of bamboo. Pandas walk on all fours with their paws turned inwards. They move slowly and hardly ever hurry.

WHAT DO PANDAS EAT?

Giant pandas feed mainly on bamboo stems and leaves. Some zoo pandas like to eat meat and bones but, in the wild, pandas move too slowly to catch most animals. Sometimes they manage to catch a bamboo rat to eat.

Bamboo is a type of giant grass, which grows about 3 metres (10 feet) tall. Bamboo stems are thicker than your finger and as hard as wood. Imagine crunching through a thick pencil and you'll see why eating bamboo stems is hard work! Pandas like the greener, more juicy stems or the young shoots best of all.

Bamboo is not very nourishing and pandas can digest only about 17 per cent of their food. So they have to eat a lot of bamboo every day to stay healthy. A panda has to spend up to 16 hours a day just eating. A bamboo diet does have some advantages though. Bamboo grows all year round, even in winter, and hardly any other animals eat bamboo.

FOOD FACTS

A panda has to eat about 15-35 kilograms (33-77 pounds) of bamboo a day to get all the goodness it needs. A panda eats about 600 bamboo stems in a day.

Zoo pandas are very fond of honey and will eat anything from chicken to chocolate.

A zoo panda once ate an iron basin.

◀ A panda has powerful jaws and big, strong cheek teeth to bite through the tough bamboo stems and get at the soft pith inside. Inside a panda's throat there is a tough lining to protect it from sharp splinters of bamboo.

▶ A panda has a sixth 'finger' on each of its front paws which helps it to hold the bamboo stems. The extra 'finger' is a tough knob below the panda's first 'finger'.

A PANDA'S DAY

A panda spends more than half the day munching, grinding and chewing its way through a huge amount of bamboo stems and leaves.

A panda does not have a special sleeping place. When it is tired, it sleeps on the ground or in a hollow tree.

Pandas are good swimmers. When it is swimming, a panda holds its head above the water and paddles fast with its legs.

From time to time, a panda rubs its bottom against a tree trunk or rock to spread scented messages for other pandas.

FINDING A MATE

A male and a female panda come together to mate. This usually happens in the spring. The female panda leaves scent marks on logs and stones. These smelly messages tell a male panda that she is ready to mate. The female also makes grunting and bleating noises at this time. A male panda answers her calls and may roar to tell other males to keep away.

After a few days, when the pandas have spent some time together, the female may allow the male to mate with her. A short while after mating, they separate and go off to live on their own again.

▲ This male panda is sniffing the scent left on a tree by a female panda.

BABY PANDAS

About five months after mating, the female panda may have one or two babies. The babies are called cubs and only one cub usually survives. The male panda does not help to look after the cub.

The female gives birth in a hollow tree or a cave. Here the cub will be safe from enemies. The newborn panda is very small; it is only about 16 centimetres (6 inches) long. It is also completely helpless and can't open its eyes.

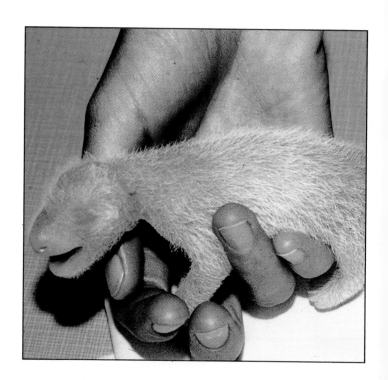

▲ When a panda is born, it is pink with some thin, white, fuzzy hair. It has no black markings at all.

◀ Zoos all over the world are trying to help their pandas to mate and have babies. But very few pandas mate in zoos so scientists often use artificial methods. These make it possible for a female panda to have a baby without mating. If enough pandas are born in zoos, it may be possible to take some of them to their natural home in China and release them into the wild.

BABY FACTS

If there is any sign of danger, the mother panda may pick up the cub in her mouth and carry it to a safe place.

When a panda is born, it weighs about the same as a small apple.

A mother panda holds her cub in her arms day and night for the first few weeks of its life. She licks her cub to keep it clean.

GROWING UP

CUB FACTS

10 minutes
Very small; helpless; cannot see; pink with some white hair.

2 weeks
Black and white markings start to show.

4 weeks
Eyes still shut; thicker black and white fur.

6-8 weeks
Eyes open; begins to crawl

3 months
Takes first steps; teeth begin to come through.

5 months
Moves around but unsteady on legs; begins to eat bamboo but will drink mother's milk as well until 9 months old.

1 year
Can move well on its own; all its teeth have come through; eats bamboo.

The tiny cub grows quickly. Each day, it sucks milk from its mother and puts on weight. When the cub is about 6 days old, patches of black fur start to grow. The black eye patches appear first. After about 35-40 days, the baby panda opens its eyes. At this stage, the mother still holds her baby in her arms most of the time.

By the time the cub is three months old, it can crawl about on its own and its teeth begin to come through. It stays close to its mother all the time.

When it is five months old, the cub weighs 10 kilograms (22 pounds) and is much too heavy for its mother to carry. The cub still sucks milk from its mother but now she starts to teach it how to eat bamboo.

In the next few months, the mother panda has to teach her cub how to survive on its own in the bamboo forest. The cub must learn how to leave its scent on rocks and logs and the best way to escape from enemies. Can you remember one of the ways in which adult pandas escape from their enemies?

When the young panda is one and a half to two years old, it leaves its mother and wanders off to look for its own area of bamboo forest to live in. When it is about five or six years old, it may find a mate and start a family of its own.

SAVE THE PANDA

There are probably only about 800-1000 giant pandas left in China today. Some scientists think there may be as few as 300-400 pandas left. Hundreds of years ago, there were bamboo forests all over China and many more pandas were able to live there. But people cut down the forests so they could build villages and grow rice on the land. People also hunted the pandas and sold their skins as sleeping mats.

Nowadays, it is against the law to hunt pandas anywhere in China. But there is a danger that pandas may be taken illegally by poachers or caught by mistake in traps used to catch other animals, such as musk deer. Twelve panda reserves have been set up to give the few remaining pandas enough room to live in peace. Scientists are making careful studies of the panda's way of life. This information will help them plan the best way to help pandas survive.

▶ Scientists trap the pandas and put them to sleep for a little while. Then they fit a collar (like the one in the picture below) around the panda's neck. The collar has a tiny radio joined to it and the scientists can pick up signals from the radio. They can follow the panda without getting too close.

BAMBOO

Another problem that puts the pandas in danger is something that happens to the bamboo which they live on. Bamboo is very unusual in that it only flowers once every 50 to 100 years. And when it has finished flowering and making seeds, it dies. There are lots of different kinds of bamboo but each kind flowers at the same time. It takes up to six years for the seeds to grow into new bamboo plants big enough for the pandas to eat.

In the past, when the bamboo flowered and died in one area, the pandas could just move to another forest. But today, the pandas have nowhere else to go. So if the bamboo in one area dies, they starve to death. In the panda reserves, the people help by feeding the pandas. Different types of bamboo are also being planted in the reserves. These bamboo plants will flower and die in different years so the pandas should always have some bamboo to eat.

◄ The World Wide Fund for Nature uses the symbol of a giant panda to remind people that animals all over the world need our help if they are to survive. A lot of work needs to be done to save the panda.

MOUNTAIN GAME

Can you help the climber to find his way back to his house at the bottom of the mountain?

To play this game, you will need a dice and some counters.

If you land on a black oval, go forward one place. If you land on a red oval, go back one place.

START
Throw one to start.

You get lost in the snow. Go back 3 places.

Find path through bamboo forest. Go forward 1 place.

Stop to watch panda eating bamboo. Miss a turn.

THE BOY WHO SAW BEI-SHUNG

BY CAROLYN GLOECKNER

Chao Tze climbed slowly up the steep mountainside. A warm breeze was blowing. New green leaves spilled from the thickets of bamboo around him. Far above, the mountain's cap of snow melted into rushing streams. Spring had come to China.

From his secret place high on the mountain, Chao Tze watched the people of his village at work in the fields below. He searched for his uncle among the tiny figures, then turned at a sudden sound behind him.

At first Chao Tze did not know what it was. He saw only glossy black fur and a small, clownish face. Then a huge black-and-white animal lumbered toward him and into a small clearing. Could this be *bei-shung,* the giant panda? The boy stared, not believing his eyes. Many in the village said that there were no more pandas in these mountains. But they were wrong, for here was *bei-shung.*

The panda's bright eyes peered out from two spots of shiny black. Chao Tze held his breath. Would the big animal see him? Were pandas dangerous? He tried to remember what he had heard and read about the panda, but his mind was too full of what he was seeing.

The panda tore a bamboo stem from the thicket and held it between his huge paws. He leaned back against a big rock and began to peel away the leaves and eat them. His small round stomach stuck out. His paws gripped the stem tightly against his furry chest. When the

as the panda ate. At last, the big animal was finished with his bamboo feast. He rose to his feet and soon vanished behind a clump of young spruce. Chao Tze watched until the panda was gone. Then, his heart pounding, he started down the mountainside thinking about the wonderful news he had to tell the people of his village. He began to hurry, slipping and sliding down the mountain trail and racing along the road towards home.

bamboo stem broke suddenly, *bei-shung* looked so surprised and funny that Chao Tze almost laughed out loud.

For a long time, the boy watched

His family and his neighbours were as excited as Chao Tze himself when he told them about the panda. The news spread quickly through the village, and people began to call him

"the boy who saw *bei-shung*."

One sunny day not long afterward, a big truck bounced down the village road. In the back were eight men, many ropes and nets, and a large cage. The driver stopped the truck in front of Chao Tze's house. He talked to Chao Tze's parents at the door.

"My name is Lim," the truck driver said. "We've come to talk to the boy who saw *bei-shung*."

Chao Tze stepped forward proudly.

"We are here to capture the panda," said the driver to Chao Tze. "Can you take us to the place where you saw him?"

Chao Tze was no longer proud. Capture *bei-shung*? No! "But the panda is very happy in the bamboo forest," he said. "You must not take him away!"

The driver's eyes were sad. "I know how you feel, Chao Tze, but for many years we have cleared the bamboo forests to make room for our farmers' fields. And without bamboo, the pandas will starve. The places where pandas can live in peace grow fewer every year. There are not many pandas remaining. We must see that these few are protected."

Chao Tze did not know what to do.

It was true that farmers in his own village were carving new fields out of the mountainsides all the time. The same thing was happening all over. But where would the men take *bei-shung?*

The driver carefully explained that in order to help pandas, scientists had to learn more about them. *Bei-shung* would be taken to a research centre for study, but he'd be well looked after.

Finally, Chao Tze decided to lead

waiting for a panda to enter one of their traps. They quickly got out a huge net and hurried towards the panda. Chao Tze turned away, for he could not bear to watch *bei-shung* struggle to escape.

The men were too busy to notice the rustlings in a spruce tree nearby. But Chao Tze noticed. What was that sound? He saw a patch of shiny black fur, and one bright little eye. Grasping a low branch, he swung himself up into the tree. There

the men to the giant panda. They took the truck halfway up the mountain and then continued on foot. The trail was steep and rocky and the men stopped often to rest. As they neared Chao Tze's secret place, the boy began to wonder if he had done the right thing. Maybe they should leave the panda alone after all.

But it was too late. There in the clearing was *bei-shung,* bamboo shoots clutched in his huge paws. The men couldn't believe their luck. Normally they had to spend days

among the dark green needles, a tiny ball of black and white clung tightly to a branch. It was a young panda, smaller even than Chao Tze's little sister.

So *bei-shung* was a mother! This little one was her cub. Chao Tze was sadder than ever. He could not, *would not,* let this baby be taken away from its home.

Saying nothing, the boy climbed down from the tree. He stood silently watching while the men prepared to carry the panda down the mountain.

And he began to worry. How would the panda cub get along without its mother? Chao Tze could not care for the baby himself.

At last the men were ready to go.

Chao Tze cried out. "Wait, there's another. A cub!"

He pointed to the tree, and two of the men quickly climbed up to reach the little panda.

The truck driver, Lim, smiled as he gently took the baby. "Today we are most fortunate. We have found not one panda, but two." Then he made Chao Tze a special promise.

"For a time, this mother and baby must stay at the research centre. Our scientists will study them. We will feed them well and make sure they are strong and healthy. Then, when the cub is old enough, we will take them to a panda reserve. There, no one is ever permitted to cut the bamboo forests. There, pandas can roam free. As much as we need land for growing food, Chao Tze, we need the beautiful panda, too."

Chao Tze thought about this promise as the truck bounced down the road towards his house. He thought about steep mountainsides where rhododendrons bloomed, where bamboo forests were so thick that no one could enter, where the panda mother and her cub would once more roam wild and free.

SPOT THE DIFFERENCE

Can you spot ten differences between these two pictures?

PANDA MASK

There are lots of ways to decorate masks. Here are a few things to try.

wool

string

straws

crayons

paint

fabric

coloured paper

Try making a mask. It's easy to do and fun to wear. All you need is a piece of card or thick paper, a length of elastic, string or lace and a pair of scissors.

Draw a basic mask shape on to the card. Remember to make two holes for your eyes and a small hole at each side of the mask. Carefully cut out your mask shape and then decide how you are going to decorate. it. Try some of the ideas in the picture on the left. When your mask is decorated, thread the elastic, string or lace through the two holes at the side of the mask. Now your mask is ready to wear!

► This mask was made by cutting out the basic shape from card and decorating it with coloured paper.

FIND THE PANDAS

There are six pandas hiding in this picture. Can you find them all?

There is one more animal in the picture. Do you know its name?

BAMBOO MAZE

Can you help this baby panda find its mother?

TRUE OR FALSE ?

Which of these facts are true and which ones are false? If you have read this book carefully, you will know the answers.

1. Giant pandas live in China.
2. Giant pandas have a long, bushy tail.

3. Giant pandas live in family groups.
4. Giant pandas are good at climbing trees.
5. Giant pandas walk fast and are always in a hurry.

6. A giant panda has a sixth 'finger' which helps it to hold bamboo stems.

7. Giant pandas eat for up to 16 hours every day.
8. Giant pandas are good swimmers.

9. When a baby panda is born, it is black and white, just like its parents.
10. A baby panda opens its eyes when it is about 2 days old.
11. A baby panda leaves its mother when it is 6 months old.

A.R.

12. Giant pandas are one of the rarest animals in the world.
13. In winter, a giant panda turns white all over.

Answers: 1. True; 2. False; 3. False; 4. True; 5. False; 6. True; 7. True; 8. True; 9. False; 10. False; 11. False; 12. False; 13. False.

31